Hear the Music

Hear the music call to you;
Hear it tell you what to do.

Roll those drums and march those feet;
Step in time and keep the beat.

Clang the cymbals, strike the sticks;
Castanets add clacks and clicks.

One and two and three and four—
March like soldiers home from war.

~Gail Fitzgerald

Reading 1E   **Fourth Edition**

bju press®
Greenville, South Carolina

Note
The fact that materials produced by other publishers may be referred to in this volume does not constitute an endorsement of the content or theological position of materials produced by such publishers. Any references and ancillary materials are listed as an aid to the student or the teacher and in an attempt to maintain the accepted academic standards of the publishing industry.

READING 1E
Hear the Music
Fourth Edition

Coordinating Authors
Ann Larson
Susan J. Lehman
Linda O. Parker
L. Michelle Rosier

Consultant
Katie Klipp

Editor
Melissa Endres

Project Manager
Lesley Morris

Design Coordinator
Michael Asire

Cover Design
Elly Kalagayan

Page Layout
Ealia Padreganda

Permissions
Sylvia Gass
Lilia Kielmeyer
Carla Thomas

Illustrators
Paula Cheadle
Tim Davis
Cory Godbey
Courtney Godbey
Holly Hannon
Keith Neely
John Roberts
Lynda Slattery
Dana Thompson
Del Thompson

Acknowledgments and photo credits appear on page 133.

Contents
Hear the Music

THE AUNTS GO MARCHING

Maurie J. Manning

From the book *The Aunts Go Marching*

The Aunts Go Marching

(Tune: "When Johnny Comes Marching Home")

Maurie J. Manning

American Folksong

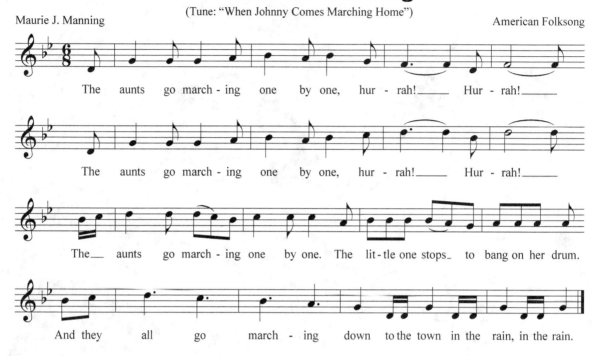

The aunts go march - ing one by one, hur - rah!___ Hur - rah!___

The aunts go march - ing one by one, hur - rah!___ Hur - rah!___

The___ aunts go march - ing one by one. The lit - tle one stops_ to bang on her drum.

And they all go march - ing down to the town in the rain, in the rain.

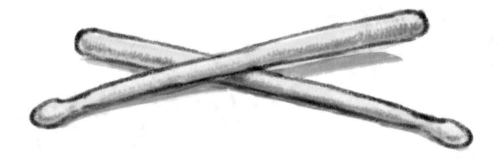

Rat a tat-tat!

Ba-rump, ba-rump,

b a - r u m p !

The aunts go marching one by one, hurrah! Hurrah!
The aunts go marching one by one, hurrah! Hurrah!
The aunts go marching one by one.
The little one stops to bang on her drum.
And they all go marching down to the town
in the rain, in the rain.

Rat a tat-tat! Rat a tat-tat! Ba-rump, ba-rump, ba-rump!

The aunts go marching two by two, hurrah! Hurrah!
The aunts go marching two by two, hurrah! Hurrah!
The aunts go marching two by two.
The little one stops to fix her shoe.
And they all go marching down to the town
in the rain, in the rain.

Rat a tat-tat! Rat a tat-tat! Ba-rump, ba-rump, ba-rump!

The aunts go marching three by three, hurrah! Hurrah!
The aunts go marching three by three, hurrah! Hurrah!
The aunts go marching three by three.
The little one stops to look and see.
And they all go marching down to the town
in the rain, in the rain.

Rat a tat-tat! Rat a tat-tat! Ba-rump, ba-rump, ba-rump!

The aunts go marching four by four, hurrah! Hurrah!
The aunts go marching four by four, hurrah! Hurrah!
The aunts go marching four by four.
The little one stops to take one more.
And they all go marching down to the town
in the rain, in the rain.

Rat a tat-tat! Rat a tat-tat! Ba-rump, ba-rump, ba-rump!

The aunts go marching five by five, hurrah! Hurrah!
The aunts go marching five by five, hurrah! Hurrah!
The aunts go marching five by five.
The little one stops to shout, "SURPRISE!"
And they all go marching down to the town
in the rain, in the rain.

Rat a tat-tat!
     Rat a tat-tat!
          Ba-rump, ba-rump, ba-rump!

The aunts go marching six by six, hurrah! Hurrah!
The aunts go marching six by six, hurrah! Hurrah!
The aunts go marching six by six.
The little one stops to pick up her sticks.
And they all go marching down to the town
in the rain, in the rain.

Rat a tat-tat!
Rat a tat-tat!
Ba-rump, ba-rump, ba-rump!

The aunts go marching seven by seven, hurrah! Hurrah!
The aunts go marching seven by seven hurrah! Hurrah!
The aunts go marching seven by seven
The little one stops to look at the heavens.

Rat a tat-tat! Rat a tat-tat! Ba-rump, ba-rump, ba-rump!

BOOM!

The aunts come marching eight by eight, hurrah! Hurrah!
The aunts come marching eight by eight, hurrah! Hurrah!
The aunts come marching eight by eight.
The little one runs to open the gate.
And they all come marching back from the town
in the rain, in the rain.

24

Rat a tat-tat! Rat a tat-tat!
Ba-rump, ba-rump, ba-rump!

BOOM!

The aunts come marching nine by nine, hurrah! Hurrah!
The aunts come marching nine by nine, hurrah! Hurrah!
The aunts come marching nine by nine.
The little one runs to join the line.
And they all come marching back from the town
in the rain, in the rain.

Rat a tat-tat!
Rat a tat-tat!
Ba-rump, ba-rump, ba-rump!

BOOM!

27

The aunts come marching ten by ten, hurrah! Hurrah
The aunts come marching ten by ten, hurrah! Hurrah
The aunts come marching ten by ten . . . .

The little one says, "Let's do it again!"
In the rain, in the rain.

Rat a tat-tat!
Rat a tat-tat!
Ba-rump,
ba-rump,
ba-rump!

BOOM!

Band Instruments

Robin E. Scroggins
illustrated by Del Thompson

A band has three groups of instruments.

Percussion

Many percussion instruments are played by tapping or beating on them to make a sound. Sometimes small children play simple percussion instruments in a rhythm band.

triangle   drum   cymbals

Brass

A musician plays each brass instrument by blowing through a metal mouthpiece. He changes the sound by moving his lips. Sometimes he changes the sound by pressing valves. A musician changes the sound of the trombone by moving the slide.

The smallest brass instruments make the highest sounds. The largest brass instruments make the lowest sounds.

French horn

trumpet

trombone

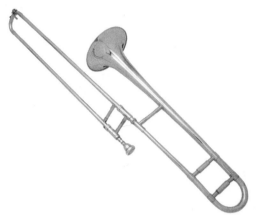

tuba

baritone

Woodwinds

Musicians play some woodwind instruments by blowing across an opening in the lip plate. They play other woodwinds by blowing through reeds. They change the sound by using their fingers to press keys or to cover holes.

The shorter instruments make higher sounds. The larger instruments make deeper sounds.

piccolo   flute

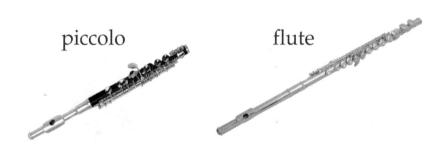

clarinet   oboe

saxophone   bassoon

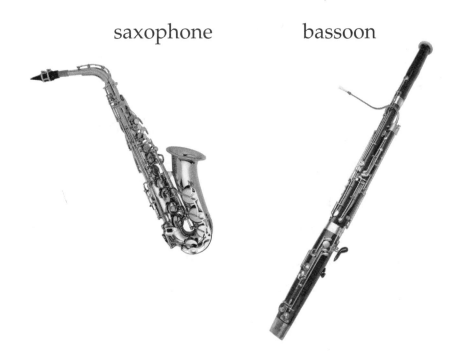

All Together Now

Jamie Turner
illustrated by Tim Davis

Let's Get Started

As the clock struck seven, sounds of scraping and clicking filled the dark room.

Trumpet was the first to scramble out of his black case. He flipped on the light. He played a long high note.

"It's time to get out! It's time to get out! It's time to get out and play music!" he sang brightly.

"Here we come! Here we come!" tooted Clarinet.

Trombone pushed his slide out as far as it would go. He squeezed some drops of oil onto it. Then he slid it quickly back and forth. "I hope we play some snappy music tonight," he said with a yawn.

"Oomph! Me too!" grunted Tuba. He settled into his seat in the back row and shuffled through his sheets of music.

French Horn and Baritone pressed their keys down lightly and spoke to the other instruments. "Let's all get seated on time tonight and surprise Mr. Baton," they said.

"All r-r-right!" rumbled Drum as he took out his list of names. "R-r-reply when I r-r-read your name!"

"Let's skip the names!" whined Oboe. "It's a waste of time. Everyone is here."

"Piccolo isn't," trilled Flute, polishing her silver coat with a soft rag.

"So what if Piccolo is missing," squeaked Oboe. "She's so little that she doesn't matter at all."

"Her shrill voice gets on my nerves," boomed Bassoon loudly.

"Yes, let's start without her," wheezed Saxophone.

"Yes! Yes!" the others tooted rudely.

Just then a small voice piped up from the back corner.

There stood Piccolo, looking at the other instruments sadly. "I always thought you were my friends," she said. Her shine was gone, and her lip plate quivered as she spoke.

The other instruments looked down in shame and pretended to be studying their music. No one said anything.

Piccolo slowly crawled back inside her small case and shut the lid with a sad little click. A tiny, muffled sob floated up from the dark, lonely corner.

"Well, come on, everyone!" snapped Oboe. "Let's get started! Mr. Baton will be here soon!"

Who Is Missing?

Mr. Baton held himself stiff and tall as he spoke to the band.

"Tonight," he said, "we are going to play a march called 'The Stars and Stripes Forever.' We will perform it this summer at the Fourth of July concert."

As Mr. Baton passed out pages of the music, the instruments buzzed with excitement.

Then he stepped to the front, tapped briskly, and raised himself up to lead. "One, two, one, two," he said.

With one swift stroke he started the instruments on the first note. The instruments swayed lightly as they played the lively march. All at once Mr. Baton stopped the music.

"Stop! Stop! This part is not right!" He frowned at the empty seat next to Flute. "We cannot do this march without Piccolo's help!" he shouted. "Where is she?"

The instruments shifted in their seats.

"I'm in here," sniffled a high, wee voice. The room became still as all eyes turned to the back corner. A red-eyed Piccolo peeked out of her little case.

"What are you doing back there?" called Mr. Baton. "Are you sick?" The other instruments gasped quietly and looked down at the floor. What would Piccolo say?

"But . . . but . . . but . . . I thought you didn't need me," she squeaked. "I'm the smallest instrument in the band, and . . ."

"Fiddlesticks!" roared Mr. Baton. Then he lowered his voice and spoke with gentleness. "Piccolo, we cannot play our music without your help," he said. "No one can play your part. Please come."

And he went back to her case and helped her out. Hand in hand they returned to the front of the room. Flute dabbed the wetness from Piccolo's keys, and Clarinet opened her music to the right page.

"Let's start over," said Mr. Baton, tapping the music stand. When it was time for Piccolo's part, Mr. Baton nodded at her. She stood and sang sweetly and brightly as Mr. Baton smiled.

When the march was over, the other instruments began clapping. "Hooray for Piccolo! Hooray for Piccolo!" they chanted joyfully.

The Baton

This baton is used to lead an orchestra or band.

This baton is used in a relay race.

Spell JOY

Jan Joss
illustrated by Keith Neely

A Happy Song

Ashley liked the song her mom led the first morning of Bible school. It had a happy sound, and it made Ashley happy when she sang it.

Jesus and others and you,
What a wonderful way to spell joy.
Jesus and others and you,
In the life of each girl and each boy.
J is for Jesus, for He has first place,
O is for others we meet face to face;
Y is for you in whatever you do,
Put yourself third, and spell JOY!

Ashley sang the song over and over in her heart as she ate her snack. She even thought of the song while her mother was telling a Bible story. At playtime, Ashley was still singing. She got in line for the swings.

Jesus and others and you,
What a wonderful way to spell joy.

I wish I could get a swing, she thought. She looked at Tim and some of the other boys in line in front of her. *The swings will all be taken. I will not get a turn.* The song in her heart stopped.

48

The next day at snack time, Ashley thought about the swings again. She hoped she would get a turn to swing. The thought of swinging brought the song back to her heart.

49

When Mrs. Miller asked the children to line up to go out and play, Marta's grandma came over to the line. "Marta and Ashley," she said, "will you please help me put the paint and brushes out for the craft time?"

"Yes, Grandma," Marta said.

"Yes, Mrs. López," Ashley said. But her heart was sad. She would not get a chance to swing at all! The song went out of her heart.

O is for Others

Mrs. López led the craft class. The children painted pictures of the Bible story they had learned that morning. They each made a frame and painted that too. Then Mrs. Miller said it was time for one more playtime.

This time I will get a swing! Ashley thought. *I will be fast. I will be first in line. I will get my turn!* She was happy, and the song about joy started in her heart again.

J is for Jesus, for He has first place,
O is for others we meet face to face;
Y is for you in whatever you do,
Put yourself third, and spell JOY!

51

When Mrs. Miller said, "Stand in line to go out," Ashley rushed to the door. She was first in line. She was in front of Reggie and Alex and Tim. She would get a swing this time!

But just then, Marta dropped her paint!
What a sight! White paint went everywhere.
Marta looked as if she might cry.

"Who will help Marta?" Mrs. López asked.
Ashley was first in line. She would get a swing
this time. But the song kept singing in her
heart. "Put yourself third and spell joy."

"I will help Marta," Ashley said. She smiled
at Marta. Marta smiled too.

As Mrs. Miller and the class left for the playground, Ashley got a clean rag. Ashley wiped paint. Marta wiped paint. They began to talk and laugh.

"Thank you for helping me," Marta said. "That makes me happy."

Ashley smiled. She started to sing. Marta sang too. "Jesus and others and you, What a wonderful way to spell JOY!"

Jan Joss, Author

Jan Joss always loved to tell stories. She won first prize in a storytelling contest when she was in seventh grade. In the summers during college, Jan enjoyed telling stories around the campfire to campers. She used her experiences as she wrote stories for children to read.

The Superduper Bamboozle Horn

Becky Davis
illustrated by Tim Davis

Bits and Parts

"I give up," said Mom. "I want to fix this tuba, but I can't even get a single note to come out of it. I might as well throw it away."

"In that case, may I have it?" asked Milly.

"Yes, you may," said Mom. "But what are you going to do with it?"

"I'm going to invent a Superduper Bamboozle Horn," said Milly.

"Oh my!" said Mom.

Milly took the tuba to her room. She took it apart until there were big parts and little parts scattered all over the floor. Then she began putting the parts here and there in her own special way.

After a while she stopped and said to herself, "What this needs is one thin part with notches in it to match this one."

There was a loud clanging from the kitchen. Milly went to see what was going on. Dad was fixing the sink. Milly watched for a while. When Dad set a broken pipe down, Milly said, "May I have that?"

"Yes, you may," said Dad. "But why does a little girl like you need a pipe?"

"I'm inventing a Superduper Bamboozle Horn," said Milly.

"Oh my!" said Dad.

Milly put the pipe in her room and went outside. Mr. Fisher was putting a used refrigerator out for the trash men to pick up.

"Mr. Fisher," Milly said, clapping her hands. "May I please have the coils from the back of that refrigerator?"

"Yes, you may," said Mr. Fisher. "But what would a little girl like you want with these worn out coils?"

"I'm inventing a Superduper Bamboozle Horn," said Milly.

"Oh my!" said Mr. Fisher.

Clutching the coils, Milly went back to her room. In a little while funny noises came from the room. Screechings and crashings and creakings and bangings filled the house.

A Special Horn

At last Milly opened the door. She held what looked like a huge tangle of twisted pretzels.

Dad blinked. Mom sat down and fanned herself. "What is that thing?" she asked.

"The Superduper Bamboozle Horn," Milly said in surprise. She put the horn to her lips and gave a mighty blast.

Mom put her hands over her ears.

"That's some horn," Dad said. "I think you had better play it outside."

"Yes, sir," Milly said.

She went outside and marched up and down in front of the house.

Mr. Fisher dropped his hose and put his hands over his ears. Mr. Fisher's beagle ran for the doghouse, howling. He got tangled in the hose and dragged the sprinkler after him.

Mrs. Glennon dropped her rake and put her hands over her ears. Her cat ran for the tree, scattering the pile of leaves on the way.

Mr. Brady dropped his paintbrush and put his hands over his ears.

Mom and Dad came running out of the house.

"What is that?" said Mr. Fisher.

"It's my Superduper Bamboozle Horn," said Milly. "Isn't it great?"

"Just great, Milly," said Mrs. Glennon, with a twinkle in her eye. "But it has one problem."

"I have something that will help," said Mom. She went into the house and came out with a small pillow. She put the pillow in the horn.

"There, Milly," she said. "Try that."

"*Blum, blah,* BLAT, BLAT, *blah, blum,*" went the horn.

Milly gave her mom a happy smile. "Thanks, Mom."

Mom and Dad went back inside the house. Mr. Fisher went back to finish watering the flowers. Mrs. Glennon went back to raking her leaves. Mr. Brady went back to painting his house. And Milly marched up and down, blowing her Superduper Bamboozle Horn.

But the cat stayed up in the tree, and the dog stayed in the doghouse.

Sounds from Softest to Loudest

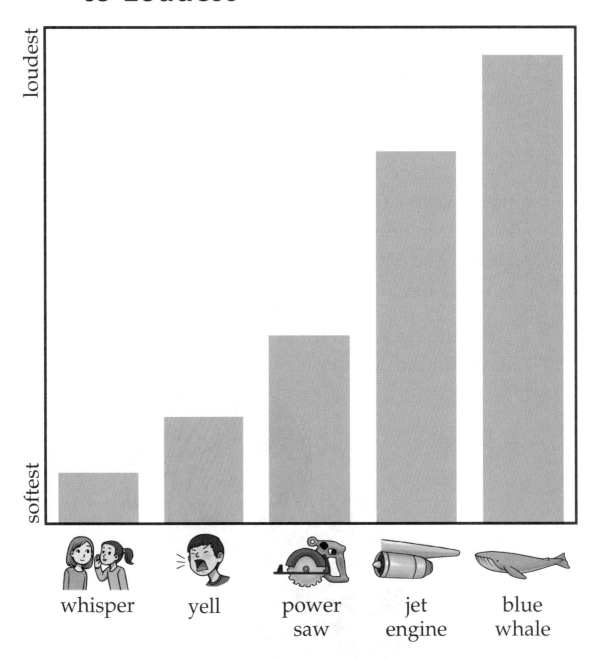

The Gift of Music

From the biography of Johann Sebastian Bach
Adapted by Muriel Murr
illustrated by John Roberts

Music Lessons

"Good job, Johann," said Christoph. "You are playing that perfectly."

Johann smiled. He loved taking music lessons from his big brother. Christoph was like a father to Johann. Their father and mother had died when Johann was just a boy.

Christoph gave Johann lessons on the clavichord and the organ. Johann loved music, and he learned quickly.

Sometimes the music Christoph gave him seemed too easy. Johann wanted to try harder music.

"May I try to play from your special book?" Johann asked. Christoph had a book of hard music that he kept on a high shelf.

"No, Johann. It is too hard for you," Christoph said.

Johann said, "I would like to try. I think I could play it."

"Maybe someday, but it's time for you to stop playing today. You need to do your schoolwork," his brother said.

Time for schoolwork. Those were the words Johann never liked to hear. Johann loved to play the clavichord, but Christoph would only let him play for a short time each day. Johann would have played music all day if Christoph would have let him.

Johann slid off the bench and went to do his schoolwork. While he worked he thought of the book on the high shelf. He was sure he could play from that special book.

One night when Christoph was in bed, Johann quietly crept to the bookshelf. He stood on a stool and got the special music book from the shelf.

Back in his bedroom, bright moonlight shone through the window. Johann got his pen and ink and began to copy the notes onto his paper. He must get the book back on the bookshelf before morning!

The Special Music Book

Every night for many, many weeks Johann crept to the bookshelf. Every night he would copy more notes from that special book. Soon there was a big stack of pages hidden under his bed.

Sometimes in the morning Johann would oversleep. And many days he was very sleepy at school.

At last, Johann finished copying the notes from the book. The thick stack of pages was safe under his bed. He waited for a chance to try the hard music.

Then one morning, Christoph went away.

"I will play the music on the clavichord now!" thought Johann.

The music was not too hard for him. Johann played all the notes right. Music floated through the house. It was such pretty music! Johann played it and forgot about everything else.

Then it happened. The door opened. Christoph came hurrying in.

"This music is much too hard for you." Christoph took the stack of pages from the clavichord.

Tears filled Johann's eyes. Then he began to weep. After all his work copying all those pages of notes, Christoph had taken them from him.

After Christoph left, Johann began to play the clavichord again. How happy he was! The pages were all gone, but he could still play every song.

Johann Sebastian Bach composed many, many songs and other works of music in his lifetime. Today, people everywhere still love to hear his music.

Bach lived from 1685 to 1750. This true account of an incident in his boyhood demonstrates the gift of music God gave to him. Later, as he matured as a Christian, he wrote hundreds of pieces of music that give praise to the Lord. He was an amazing composer and a talented performer on violin, organ, and other instruments. Someone said of him, "He can play anything." Bach wrote his last piece of music while sick and lying in bed; he dictated the music to his son-in-law. The words begin, "Before Your throne, my God, I stand."

Johann Sebastian Bach
1685–1750

Johann Sebastian Bach was born into a very musical German family. His father was the town musician. His parents died by the time he was ten. His brother took care of him.

Bach became one of the greatest composers of all time. He wrote hundreds of pieces of music that give praise to God. He played the violin, organ, and other instruments.

The Grasshopper and the Ant

A fable
Adapted by Gail Fitzgerald
illustrated by Holly Hannon

On the hottest day of the summer, Mr. Grasshopper lay in the shade. He played his fiddle a while. He slept a while. He played his fiddle some more.

Meanwhile, out in the sun, the ants were quite busy. The biggest ant was working hard. The middle-sized ants were working hard. The smallest ant was working hard. Each was busy gathering food for the winter.

I'm smarter than the ants, Mr. Grasshopper thought. *It is much nicer to stay in the shade than to work in the sun.*

He called to the biggest ant. "Why do you work so hard?"

"I am storing up food for the winter," said the ant. "You would be wise to do the same."

The grasshopper picked up his fiddle and began to play a happy tune. "Winter is far away," he said. "Come and sing with me."

"Winter will come sooner than you think," said the ant. He went on about his work, but the grasshopper only fiddled faster.

75

Days went by. The harder the ants worked, the faster Mr. Grasshopper fiddled.

By and by the days began to grow shorter. The leaves began to grow browner. The nights began to grow nippy.

Still Mr. Grasshopper fiddled. The sound of his music filled the air. But the ants did not stop to hear him. They only worked harder.

Then one day Mr. Grasshopper woke to see snow falling. He shivered in his summer coat.

I am freezing, and I am very hungry, he thought. *I have no money to buy food. I will hop around and look for something to eat.*

Mr. Grasshopper hopped to the field by the big oak tree. There were no ants in sight. There was no food in sight. He sighed and turned away. He put his fiddle to his chin and started a sad tune. *The ants are smarter than I,* he thought. *They worked while I played.*

There is a time to work and a time to play.

The Amazing Ant

I can lift more than three times my weight.

The queen ant is the head of the ant community.

I lead other ants to food and alert them of danger.

I eat nectar, seeds, fungus, or other insects.

I hunt for food and care for baby ants in the nest.

I have a large head, long antennae, and powerful jaws.

I live in underground nests, in mounds, or in trees.

The Bremen Town Musicians

A folk drama
Retold by Karen Wilt and Janet Snow
illustrated by Dana Thompson

Characters

Robin, the narrator

Donkey

Dog

Cat

Rooster

Innkeeper

Robber 1

Robber 2

Act I

Robin: I am just a little bird. But this is what I saw and heard. One morning, not too long ago, a tired old donkey came down this road.

Donkey: It is not so. It cannot be true. I am not too old to work. "Go look for another home," my master said. Hee-haw. I will look for work myself. I can sing. I will go to Bremen Town.

Dog: What is that you say, my friend?

Donkey: I am going to Bremen to be a town musician. My master thinks I am too old to work.

Dog: My master, too. He tells me I am too old to herd the sheep! I have been thinking about what to do.

Donkey: Come with me! Can you sing?

Dog: Sing? Yes, I can sing. We can sing together!

Robin: The two friends set off down the road together. I went from tree to tree to watch them. Just then I saw a sight that made my legs weak. By the side of the road sat an old cat, washing her paws.

Donkey: Good morning, Cat. We are on our way to Bremen.

Dog: We will be the town musicians. Our masters say that we are too old to work.

Cat: What about me? May I come too? I am too old to chase mice any more.

Donkey: Yes, you may, if you can sing.

Cat: I can sing quite well! What will we sing? Let us sing about mice.

Dog: I would like to sing about a nice tasty bone.

Donkey: Mice and bones! We can do better than that. Let us sing about oats and hay!

Robin: The others did not think much of that idea. The three friends thought of different songs. They went up a hill and down again, singing happily. Soon the three musicians came upon a rooster sitting on a fence.

Rooster: Cock-a-doodle-doo! Cock-a-doodle-doo! Oh, what shall I do? I must sing while I can, for tonight I will be dinner.

Donkey: Such a noise you make, my friend! What can the matter be?

Rooster: Every morning for many a year I have crowed at the sun's first light. Now my master tells me I am too old to be of any use.

Cat: You are not too old to sing.

Dog: We are musicians. Come with us.

Rooster: Cock-a-doodle-doo! I will be a musician too!

Robin: The four musicians had no money and no food, but still they sang as they went down the road to Bremen.

Act II

Rooster: We are musicians.

Dog: We want to sing at the inn.

Innkeeper: I cannot pay you to sing. Robbers stole every cent I had.

Cat: Can we sleep here tonight? We are on our way to Bremen to become musicians.

Innkeeper: Not tonight, for the inn is full. But there is a deserted house down the road. You may stay there.

Robin: The musicians followed the dark road and found the path to the house.

Donkey: *(Looking through the dirty windowpane.)* This must be the place.

Dog: What do you see?

Donkey: Coins and gems! It is the robbers!

Cat: Dear me. Meow, meow!

Donkey: Now, now, Cat. Hush! I have a plan that will make the robbers leave this place.

Robin: The musicians came near the donkey to hear the plan.

Donkey: Everyone, hop on my back. First you, Dog.

Cat: I'll be next.

Rooster: Here I go to the top.

Donkey: Now, friends, let us sing.

All: Hee-haw, Hee-haw!
   Grrr-ruff, Grrr-ruff!
   Meow, Meow, Meow!
   Cock-a-doodle-doo!

Act III

Robin: Such a noise those musicians made! Their loud song made the robbers jump from their seats.

Robber 1: What was that?

Robber 2: Such a noise I have never heard!

Robin: The robbers ran out the door, deep into the woods. And the musicians tumbled into the house.

Rooster: Look at the gems!

Dog: Look at the food!

Cat: Look at the money!

Robin: The musicians ate until they could eat no more. Then they looked for places to sleep.

Dog: I will sleep near the door.

Cat: I will sleep by the fire.

Donkey: I will sleep on this pile of straw.

Rooster: I will sleep up on the roof beam.

Robin: By this time, out in the woods, the robbers were feeling brave again.

Robber 1: It was silly to let something frighten us.

Robber 2: We should not have run away.

Robber 1: You wait here. I will go back and see what made the noise.

Robin: So the robber crept back inside. He saw Cat's glowing eyes and mistook them for hot coals. He bent down to blow on them.

Cat: Meow! Hiss! I will scratch you for that.

Robber 1: Help! Help!

Robin: The noise that they made woke up the other musicians. Dog growled and bit the robber's leg. Donkey kicked him. Rooster crowed from the high beam. The robber broke away and ran back to the woods.

Robber 2: What happened? You are pale!

Robber 1: A lion was by the fire. It scratched
   my face. A monster bit my leg. I was hit by
   a club, and a lady screamed.

Robber 2: We must get out of here fast.

Robin: The robbers ran away, never to come
   back. The musicians took the coins and
   gems back to the innkeeper. He gave them
   the house. They never did go to Bremen to
   become town musicians. They spent the rest
   of their days in the house in the woods.
   And they made music every night.

All: Hee-haw, Hee-haw!
   Grrr-ruff, Grrr-ruff!
   Meow, Meow, Meow!
   Cock-a-doodle-doo!

Animal Sounds

The songs and calls of birds are used to claim their living spaces. They also warn of danger.

Whales and seals use whistles, clicks, songs, and calls to keep track of others in their group.

Chimpanzees make about a dozen sounds. Each sound means something to the chimpanzee.

My Sister, Rita

Bobby Jones

Mike's Sister

Mike sat under a tree by himself. He did not want to play with his friends. He just wanted to go home.

"What's the matter, Mike?"

Mike looked up. It was his teacher, Miss Phillips. "I don't feel good," said Mike. "May I go home?"

"No, Mike. You must stay at school until two o'clock," said Miss Phillips. She was quiet for a moment. Then she said, "Have the children been mean again?"

Mike did not answer. Miss Phillips had seen the other kids making fun of his sister, Rita, before. He wanted to speak with Miss Phillips, but he felt like crying. He did not want to be a baby.

"Mike," said Miss Phillips, "I think we should speak to your mom after school today. Is that okay with you?"

Mike smiled. He liked Miss Phillips. She was always glad to help people. "Yes," he said, "that's fine. Thanks, Miss Phillips."

Miss Phillips smiled. "I have a plan," she said, "and it just might work!"

After school Mike sat at the big round table with his mom and Miss Phillips. His mom looked unhappy.

Miss Phillips spoke. "The children don't know what it means to be disabled. They only know that Mike's sister is different from them. I wish we could help them understand. Rita needs love just like the other children."

Mrs. Fitch looked at Mike. "You love Rita, don't you, son?" she said.

"Yes, I love Rita," said Mike. "She's my sister. But my friends make fun of her. Sometimes they play like they are disabled. Sometimes they tease that I am disabled too."

"That's not good," said Mrs. Fitch. "Rita can't do some of the things they can do, but she is very special to us."

"Yes, but how can we show my friends?" said Mike.

Rita Comes to School

The next morning Rita came to school with Mike and their mom. Mike took his sister's hand and led her to the front of the class. Rita patted Mike's back. Then she pulled his hair. "Ha, ha!" she laughed. "Ha, ha, ha!"

All the children laughed too. They laughed and whispered and pointed.

"You've all seen my sister, Rita," said Mike. He did not look at the class. He looked at the floor.

Mike's mother spoke up. All the children were quiet.

"As you can see," said Mrs. Fitch, "Rita is a special girl. She is twelve years old, but she can't count to twenty. She can't spell her own name."

The children looked at Rita. She just smiled at them. Then she laughed and waved. Mike looked at the floor.

Rita saw an apple on Miss Phillips's desk. She reached for it. "Pretty," she said.

The children watched Rita and Miss Phillips.

"You may have my apple, Rita," said Miss Phillips. "I hope you like it."

Rita took a big bite of the apple. She patted Miss Phillips's arm. Then she dropped the apple on the floor. The children laughed.

Mike looked at the floor. He wanted to go home.

"Rita is not like other children," said Mrs. Fitch. "God made her just as she is. We love her just as she is. Rita loves God too. And she loves everyone she meets. She can't spell or count, but she can love."

"There is something else Rita can do," said Miss Phillips. "It is a surprise. I think you will like it."

Mrs. Fitch sat at the keyboard. Rita jumped up and down. She clapped her hands. "Sing!" she said. "Sing! Sing!"

Mrs. Fitch began to play. Rita was still. She smiled at the class. She took Mike's hand. He looked up slowly and smiled at his sister.

Then Rita closed her eyes and sang. Her voice was quiet and sweet.

Jesus loves me! this I know,
For the Bible tells me so;

Mike wanted to cry, but he was not sad. He wanted to cry because he loved his special sister. Suddenly, he began to sing too.

Little ones to Him belong;

Rita opened her eyes and looked at Mike. She smiled and patted his arm.

Miss Phillips sang with Rita and Mike.

They are weak, but He is strong.

One by one, Mike's friends began to sing along.

Yes, Jesus loves me,
Yes, Jesus loves me,
Yes, Jesus loves me,
The Bible tells me so.

When the song was over, no one said anything. Rita closed her eyes and sang by herself one more time.

Yes, Jesus loves me,
The Bible tells me so.

For the Lord to Hear

Eileen M. Berry
illustrated by Cory Godbey

To Be Perfect

Cory opened his piano book and sighed. Only three more days until he would play his song in church.

He stared at the page and then down at the keyboard. Carefully he placed his fingers on the keys and played the first six notes. "Holy, Holy, Holy!" He thought of the words as he played. Then he stopped and looked out the window.

Mom came in and stood by the piano. "Don't stop; it sounds nice," she said with a smile. "Sunday's the big day, isn't it?"

Cory nodded without looking up.

Mom kept watching him. "What's the matter, Cory?" she asked.

"I don't think I want to play, Mom," he said. "Can you call Mrs. Howard and tell her I can't do it?"

"But your song sounds really good," said Mom. "You've worked hard on it. Why don't you want to play?"

Cory gazed down at his hands in his lap. "Last night I dreamed I was playing in church," he said. "I made a lot of mistakes. People were laughing at me."

"But, Cory, that was just a bad dream," said Mom. "You don't need to let that scare you."

"But what if it really happens? I don't want to make any mistakes. I want my song to be perfect."

Mom sat down beside him on the piano bench. She was silent for a moment. Cory stared at the black and white notes on the page until they looked blurry. He blinked and quickly wiped his hand across his eyes.

Suddenly Mom stood up. "I'll be right back," she said. "I'm going to get something."

To Give My Best

Mom came back with a card in her hand. "Do you remember this?" she asked. She handed the card to Cory.

Cory laughed. "Did I draw this?"

Mom smiled. "When you were only three," she said. "You gave it to me for Mother's Day."

"What is this a picture of? It just looks like a big bunch of scribbles."

"You said it was a picture of me working in my garden," said Mom. She laughed with him this time.

Cory put the card up on the piano. "It's a really bad drawing," he said. "You kept it all this time?"

"All this time," said Mom. "It was special to me because you made it for me."

Cory was quiet for a moment. *What does all of this have to do with my song?*

Then Mom said, "Are you playing your song for the people at church or for the Lord?"

Cory thought hard. "Well . . . for the Lord," he said at last.

"Then the Lord will look at your song the way I look at this card," said Mom. "I look at it and think about a boy that I love. I think about a boy who wanted to give me something he made just for me." Mom smiled.

"But if I make a mistake, other people besides God will hear," said Cory.

"They might," said Mom. "You should practice well and try very hard not to make a mistake. But even if you do, God will still be pleased."

Cory sat up taller on the bench.

"God sees into your heart," Mom said. "He sees the 'best' that you are giving Him with your heart."

Mom patted Cory on the arm and stood up. "I'd better let you practice a little more," she said. She went to put the card away.

Cory turned back to his music. He looked at the words:

Holy, Holy, Holy! Lord God Almighty!
All Thy works shall praise Thy name,
  in earth, and sky, and sea;
Holy, Holy, Holy! Merciful and Mighty!
God in Three Persons, blessed Trinity!

Then he began to play the song—just for the Lord to hear.

1 Corinthians 10:31

Do all to the
glory of God.

—1 Corinthians 10:31

The Popcorn Shop

Eileen M. Berry
Adapted for choral reading
illustrated by Cory Godbey

Teacher: When I walk along the block
　　　　　By the popcorn shop
　　　　　I can hear the butter sizzle in the
　　　　　　　pan.

Child: *Pop–pop!*

Teacher: And the sweet-and-salty scent
　　　　　Makes me want to stop
　　　　　For a little chat with Pat
　　　　　　the popcorn man.

Child: *Pop–pop!*

Teacher: Any flavor that you please,

Child: *(softly) Pop–pop–pop!*
    Pop–pop–pop!

Teacher: Caramel, cinnamon, and cheese,

All: *(louder) Pop–pop–pop!*
    Pop–pop–pop!

Teacher: Pat the popcorn man has got it
        popped, you know.

Child: *Pop!*

Child: *Pop!*

Teacher: So if I have change to spare,
    I've just got to swap
    For a bag of popcorn, fresh and
      hot to go.

All: *(loudly) Pop–pop!*

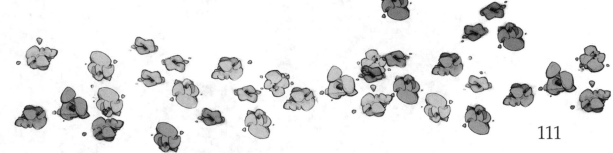
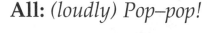

Our God Gives a Song

Taken from Acts 16:16–34
Retold by Gail Fitzgerald

The men were unhappy. They did not like to hear Paul and Silas preach about God. The men did not want to see people saved. All they wanted was money.

"These men upset the town. We can't agree with the things they teach. They must not go unpunished!" the ungodly men said.

By then the mob was angry too. They jumped upon Paul and Silas. The rulers of the town tore the robes right off God's men.

"Beat these men!" the rulers ordered.

Many times the whips were unfairly used on the men's backs. The people still were angry.

"Throw the men into jail until we decide what to do with them!" the unholy men shouted.

Paul and Silas were cast into the dark, damp jail. The jailer did not want the men to escape. He put their feet in the stocks. The stocks were shut tight. Then the jailer left. Paul and Silas were alone in the dark, damp cell. *Had God forgotten His children?*

Paul and Silas did not think so. At midnight they prayed to God. They sang praises to Him. The other men in the jail heard them sing. *Had God also heard them?*

Suddenly the ground began to rumble. The jail began to shake. Doors opened. The chains fell off the men. God had heard His children singing. *God had not forgotten Paul and Silas.*

The keeper of the jail had been sleeping. He awoke with a start. He saw the open doors.

"The men have escaped. The rulers will take my life. I will end my life myself," the jailer said to himself. Quickly he took out his sword.

"Stop!" shouted Paul with a loud voice. "Do not harm yourself. We are all here."

The jailer quickly snatched up a light. Trembling, he went to see Paul and Silas. What God did these men have? The thankful jailer fell down before God's men.

"Sirs, what must I do to be saved?"

"Trust in the Lord Jesus. You and your house will be saved."

The jailer was glad to hear what they said. Gently he washed the men's backs. Then he took Paul and Silas to his home. He gave them food to eat. He gathered the people of his house together. He wanted to hear more about the God that could give songs in the night.

Paul and Silas were glad to speak about Jesus. That night the jailer and all of his house trusted in God. God gave them a song too. It was the song of souls set free.

The Singing Fence

Milly Howard

Bamboo Poles

"May I go too, Grandfather?" Maya asked.

Grandfather Kai smiled. "Yes, you may come," he said. "Get in, Little Butterfly."

Maya went around the battered pickup truck and scrambled in. "Where are we going, Grandfather?" she asked.

"To get some bamboo from Green Willow Creek, Little Butterfly," he said.

"Are we going fishing?" Maya asked.

"No, not today," he said. His eyes twinkled in amusement. "But if you listen, you can hear the sound of crickets eating."

Maya listened. She wanted to hear the sound of crickets eating. At last she could be silent no longer. "Are you making bamboo tables?" Maya asked.

"No, not today," he repeated. "But if you listen, you can hear the sound of bees sipping nectar."

Maya listened. She tried to hear the sound of bees sipping nectar. At last she could be silent no longer.

"Then why do you need bamboo from Green Willow Creek?" Maya asked.

"Just because," said Grandfather Kai. "If you listen, you can hear the sound of rabbits twitching their noses."

Maya listened. She did not hear the sound of rabbits twitching their noses, but she did not speak again.

When they reached the creek, Grandfather
Kai cut the long, tall bamboo poles. Maya used
one of the poles to balance herself as she
tiptoed across a log. She used one of the poles
to push herself up, up, into the air. And one by
one, she put them in the back of the pickup.

"This will do just fine," Grandfather Kai said.
"You have been a big help, Maya."

"Thank you, Grandfather," Maya said. "But
what am I helping you do?"

"You will see," Grandfather said.

One by One

The pickup bounced and rattled back to Maya's house. Grandfather parked in the back. He and Maya took the poles out, one by one.

And Grandfather cut them one by one. His hatchet rose and fell in the air. At last the poles were done. Grandfather pounded some into the ground, one by one. Maya watched as he tied long poles crosswise to the ones in the ground.

"Is it a cage?" she asked.

"No, it is not a cage," Grandfather said.

He tied other bamboo poles on the crossed poles. The short poles lined up like skinny pipes.

"Is it something to water the garden?" Maya asked.

"No, it is not something to water the garden," Grandfather Kai said. He pounded another pole into place.

"Is it a fence?" Maya asked.

"You could say it is a fence," Grandfather Kai said. He pounded the last pole into place. Then he began to cut holes into the poles.

Maya's eyes were very big. "Why are you cutting holes in the fence, Grandfather?" she asked.

"If you listen, you will hear," Grandfather said.

Maya put her hand over her mouth. She did not say anything for a while. She listened.

The wind whistled gently in the garden. A faint sound drifted on the air. Maya listened harder. Grandfather cut some more holes in the bamboo. The sound became louder. It went up and down like the notes of a song.

"The fence is singing!" Maya said.

"Yes, Little Butterfly," Grandfather said. "This is a Singing Fence. And if you listen, you will hear the song of the wind."

"I will listen, Grandfather," Maya said, clapping her hands. "I cannot hear the sound of crickets eating. I cannot hear the sound of bees sipping nectar. I cannot hear the sound of rabbits twitching their noses. But I can hear the song of the wind."

The Pickety Fence

David McCord
illustrated by Paula Cheadle

The pickety fence
The pickety fence
Give it a lick it's
The pickety fence
Give it a lick it's
A clickety fence
Give it a lick it's
A lickety fence
Give it a lick
Give it a lick
Give it a lick
With a rickety stick
Pickety
Pickety
Pickety
Pick

124

Glossary

A

aunt
Aunt Mary is my mother's sister.

B

bal·ance
I can balance on one foot.

ba·ton
The band leader held up his baton.

bat·tered
The battered truck had many dents.

C

cage
A bird is in the cage.

clav·i·chord
A clavichord is like a piano.

crick·et
A cricket chirps in the evening.

cross·wise
Dan laid the poles crosswise to form an X.

D

dis·a·bled
The disabled boy got a new wheelchair.

don·key
Jesus rode a donkey into Jerusalem.

draw·ing
Mom liked my drawing of our house.

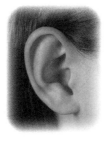

E

ears
We use our ears to hear.

earth

God made the earth and sky.

F

field

The farmer grows corn in his field.

floor

Mom swept the kitchen floor.

frame

The picture is in a frame.

G

H

hatch·et

Dad used a hatchet to cut off the tree branch.

herd

The rancher has a large herd of cattle.

I

in·stru·ment

The trumpet is a musical instrument.

J

K

key·board

A piano has a keyboard with black and white keys.

L

laugh

Dad will laugh when I tell him my joke.

M

me·ow

Kittens meow when they are hungry.

mob

A mob of people gathered in front of the bank.

morn·ing

The sun comes up in the morning.

mu·si·cian

After the concert, we met the musician.

N

notch·es

The man cut notches in the log.

O

old

The old shoe needs to be repaired.

or·gan

An organ has more than one keyboard.

P

per·cus·sion

A drum is a percussion instrument.

pi·an·o

Mrs. White plays the piano
at her church.

pic·ture

I have a picture of my dogs.

prac·tice

I practice the flute every day.

pret·zel

A pretzel is a salty snack.

Q

quiv·er

Sally's lips quiver when she starts to cry.

R

re·frig·er·a·tor
A refrigerator keeps food cold.

S

scrib·bles
The paper was covered with pencil scribbles.

sword
The sword has a sharp blade.

T

tan·gle
The kite string was in a tangle.

tu·ba
The tuba can make a deep sound.

U

V

W

whis·tle

I heard the wind whistle through the trees.

X

Y

Z

Acknowledgments

"JOY" by Sally Lewis. Copyright © 1945. Crawford Broadcasting Company, Blue Bell, PA. Reprinted with permission from The Young People's Church of the Air.

"The Pickety Fence" From ONE AT A TIME by David McCord. Copyright © 1952 by David McCord. By permission of Little, Brown and Company. All rights reserved.

"The Aunts Go Marching", written and illustrated by Maurie J. Manning. Copyright © 2003 by Maurie J. Manning. Reprinted by permission of S©ott Treimel NY.

Photo Credits

The following agencies and individuals have furnished materials to meet the photographic needs of this textbook. We wish to express our gratitude to them for their important contribution.

Suzanne Altizer
Bigstock
BJU Photo Services
Getty Images
Hemera Technologies
PhotoDisc
Dave Schuppert

SuperStock
Thinkstock
Carla Thomas
Wikipedia
www.arttoday.com

PhotoDisc/Getty Images 33 (left, center), 34 (both), 35 (top, bottom left), 36 (both), 37 (all); **Carla Thomas** 33 (right), 35 (bottom right), 55; **Wikipedia/ Public Domain** 73 (both); © **Gary Humfrey/Image from Bigstock.com** 91 (top left); © **John Warden/SuperStock** 91 (right); **Menoj Shah/Stone/Ghetty Images** 91 (bottom left)

Glossary

BJU Photo Services 125 (balance), 126 (ear), 129 (organ); **PhotoDisc/Getty Images** 125 (baton), 126 (cricket, donkey, drawing), 128 (trumpet), 130 (piano, puppies), 131 (tuba); **Suzanne Altizer** 125 (cage); **www.arttoday.com** 127 (hatchet), 130 (pretzel); **Hemera/Thinkstock** 128 (keyboard); **Carla Thomas** 129 (shoe), 131 (scribbles); © **Hemera Technologies, Inc. All rights reserved.** 130 (frame), 131 (sword); **Dave Schuppert** 131 (refrigerator)